COLOR MY OV
MONSTER STORY

MW00903679

AN IMMERSIVE, CUSTOMIZABLE
COLORING BOOK FOR KIDS (THAT RHYMES!)

BRIAN C HAILES

For information about permission to reproduce selections from this book, please write Permissions, Epic Edge Publishing, 1934 Fielding Hill Ln, Draper, UT 84020.

www.epicedgepublishing.com

Library of Congress Cataloging-in-Publication Data
Color My Own Monster Story: An Immersive, Customizable Coloring Book for Kids (That Rhymes!)
Written by Brian C Hailes

p. cm.
Summary: Bounce, crawl or slither your way into a scary and diverse world of monsters! Swing from tree limbs, blast into outer space, or swim out of terrifying swamps—the possibilities are endless . . . when you're a monster. And let's face it, you are. Sharpen your coloring skills. Hang out with silly, wacky and downright frightful beasts to your creature heart's content. And customize this strange tale with your very own name and other characteristics to become the monster (or monsters) of your own rhyming dreams! Bedtime will never be the same. (And good luck going to sleep afterwards . . . just kidding! Or am I?)

A fun, interactive coloring trip that will slap you with a tentacle or throw you into the hay—you just never know what will happen with friends like these! Grab your crayons, markers or pencils, and grease up your dragon scales, little monsters. It's time to forget about time . . . and have a great time!

(Intended for children ages 6-12 . . . or all kids at heart)

1. Childrens—Coloring Activity Books. 2. Childrens—Monsters
3. Childrens—Fiction
II. Hailes, Brian C., ill. III. Title.

Paperback ISBN-13: 978-1-951374-31-0
Hardback ISBN-13: 978-1-951374-32-7

Printed in the USA
Designed by Epic Edge Publishing

10 9 8 7 6 5 4 3 2 1

Monsters are a bunch of crazies livin' in a crazy world . . .
So yeah, we're all monsters.

— B.C. Hailes

COLOR MY OWN
MONSTER STORY

AN IMMERSIVE, CUSTOMIZABLE
COLORING BOOK FOR KIDS (THAT RHYMES!)

STARRING: _____
(your name)

Monsters are those creatures

Hiding inside everyone;

They're zany, unpredictable;

And, above all, they LOVE fun!

My monster name is _____ ,
(your monster name)

And I like to play in groups;

With freaks, chompers, _____ ,
(kooks, spooks or loons)

And puffs that look like ice cream scoops.

Some monsters might look scary

On the outside, but they're all show;

Pay no mind to tooth, wing, claw,

Or the _____ that some blow.
(fire, flames, or bad breath)

_____ , once you get to know them,
(Friendly, Chummy or Tender)
They're all truly teddy bears;

The trick is getting close enough . . .

Before they singe your hairs.

Some dress up, or try too hard

To ＿＿＿＿＿＿＿＿＿＿＿ little children;
(frighten, startle or disgust)

The ones you really should avoid,

Are those that keep well-hidden!

Goofy monsters _____ your time,
(steal, waste or cheat)

Or pretend there's no such thing;

They gamble away your money,

Clothing, assets and your bling!

The ones that think they're _____
(smart, clever or wise)

Will play with dangerous mixtures;

And blow the house to smithereens!

You'd better save the pictures!

Behemoths from the _____,
(deep, sea or blue)

May well deserve respect;

Particularly from those with firsthand knowledge

What it's like to be shipwrecked!

However, such beasts rarely _____,
(appear, surface or arise)

And when they do, you're done;

For no one can escape such odds,

And it's futile to try and run.

Try to make a pet, and you

Might not live throughout the day;

Monsters don't like _____ ,
(cages, fences or shelters)

And they don't like to obey.

So save your treats and kennels,

leashes, dog pens, collars, tags—

On second thought, you can leave

The treats and laden grocery bags.

Monsters like to _____ together,
(travel, sightsee or voyage)

Whenever they possibly can;

But getting them in sync is tough,

As none of them like to plan.

They also enjoy tinkering

With dangerous, high-tech gadgets;

Just don't record any of their

_____ , disgusting habits!

Born of science or in the woods,

Their _____ is nigh unmatched;
(diversity, variance or distinction)

But their mode of operation

Tends toward awful schemes to hatch!

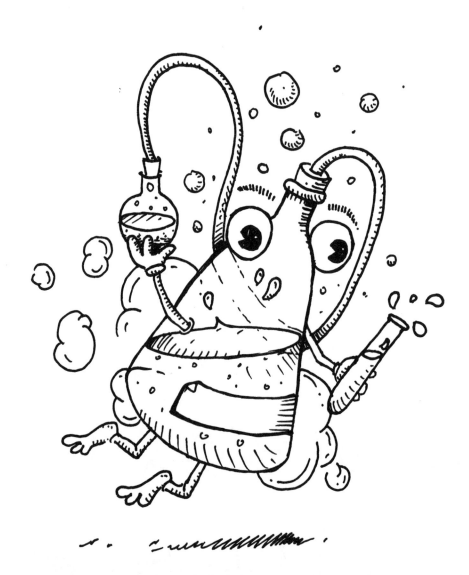

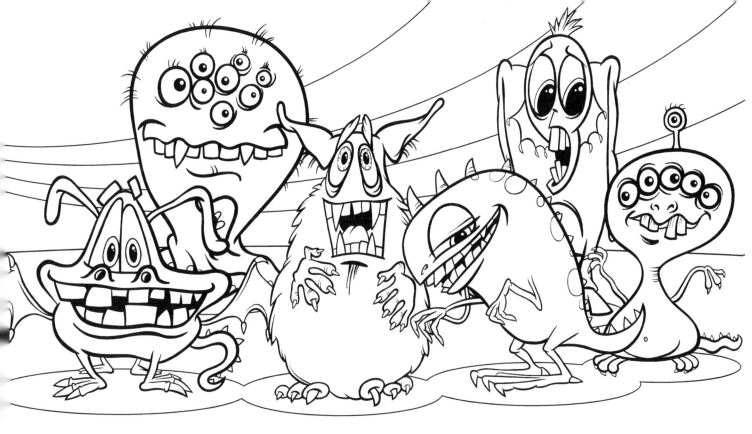

Some are terrifying, icky or _____ ;
(base, rank or mean)

Others, funny, zealous or bold.

They've been around for ages;

(But, for obvious reasons)

Their histories mostly go untold.

Which monster is your favorite?

_____ name is _____ .
(His, Her or Its)   (your best friend's name)

Monsters can be found in _____ ,
(caves, holes or dens)

Or flailing about on vines;

They populate much of outer space;

Or crawl from swamps or abandoned mines.

Personally, I live in a _____ ,
(cavern, marshland or monster house)

Where everyone knows my name.

I'm rather well known for my _____ ;
(odor, shrieking
or underbite)

That's my foremost claim to fame.

Monsters eat like old, fat kings;

'Cause everything's on the menu:

Knights and rats and _____ ;
(your favorite monster food)

(Just don't eat your nephew)

The nastiest morsel I've ever tried,

Was _____ glazed with butter.
(the grossest food you can think of)

Still, I gulped it down, slimy skin and all . . .

And my tummy made a flutter.

Monsters aren't like everyone else;

We pride ourselves on being different;

Even if that means we must be

Rowdy, crude, irreverant.

We bounce or slither, clamor, creep;

Wherever it is we please;

No one can _____ us,
(control, command or micromanage)

At least, that is, with ease.

I'm the _____ one.
(your color)

Monsters come in all shapes, sizes,

Hideous, hilarious, spry;

You can be a giant, _____
(worm, serpent or dragon)

Or the office funny guy!

Perhaps that's why we're so appealing,

We can become anyone.

Take you, for example. What's your jam?

. . . Let's have some monster fun!

THE END

OTHER "COLOR MY OWN" TITLES NOW AVAILABLE!

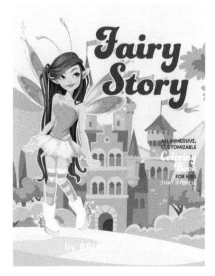

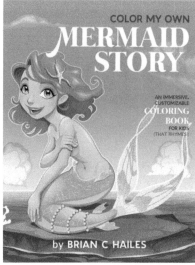

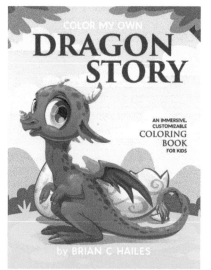

ABOUT THE AUTHOR

BRIAN C HAILES, creator of Draw It With Me (www.drawitwithme.com), is also the award-winning writer/illustrator of over forty-five (and counting) novels, children's picture books, comics and graphic novels, including Blink: An Illustrated Spy Thriller Novel, Devil's Triangle, Dragon's Gait, Skeleton Play, Don't Go Near the Crocodile Ponds, If I Were a Spaceman, Here, There Be Monsters, Heroic, Passion & Spirit, Continuum (Arcana Studios), as well as McKenna, McKenna, Ready to Fly, and Grace & Sylvie: A Recipe for Family (American Girl), among others. In addition to his publishing credits, Hailes has also illustrated an extensive collection of fantasy, science fiction, and children's book covers as well as interior magazine illustrations. Hailes has received numerous awards for his works from across the country, including Winner of the L. Ron Hubbard Illustrators of the Future contest out of Hollywood. His artwork has also been featured in the 2017-2020 editions of Infected By Art.

Hailes studied illustration and graphic design at Utah State University where he received his Bachelor of Fine Arts degree, as well as the Academy of Art University in San Francisco.

He currently lives in Salt Lake City with his wife and four boys, where he continues to write, paint and draw regularly. More of his work can be seen at HailesArt.com

Other Titles Available from
Epic Edge Publishing

Illustrated Novels	Graphic Novels / Comics	Childrens Picture Books	Anthologies	Non-Fiction

Blink: An Illustrated Spy Thriller Novel
by Brian C Hailes

Devil's Triangle: The Complete Graphic Novel
by Brian C Hailes
& Blake Casselman

If I Were a Spaceman: A Rhyming Adventure Through the Cosmos
by Brian C Hailes
& Tithi Luadthong

Cresting the Sun: A Sci-fi / Fantasy Anthology Featuring 12 Award-Winning Short Stories
by Brian C Hailes,
Rick Bennett
& Nicholas Adams

Draw It With Me: The Dynamic Female Figure
(Available 2020!)
by Brian C Hailes

Avila
(Available 2021!)
by Robert J Defendi
& Brian C Hailes

Dragon's Gait
by Brian C Hailes

Here, There Be Monsters
by Brian C Hailes
& Tithi Luadthong

Heroic: Tales of the Extraordinary
by Blake Casselman,
David Farland,
Michael Stackpole
& more

DIWM 2020 Annual 1
(Available 2020!)
by Brian C Hailes,
Heather Edwards
& more

Don't Go Near the Crocodile Ponds
by Brian C Hailes

KamiKazi
by John English
& Brian C Hailes

Skeleton Play
by Brian C Hailes

Can We Be Friends?
by Edie New
& Cindy Hailes

Passion & Spirit: The Dance Quote Book
by Brian C Hailes

CPSIA information can be obtained
at www.ICGtesting.com
Printed in the USA
BVHW051727160920
588928BV00013B/603